*This Book
belongs to the Library of
King Edward VI's
Grammar School,
Guildford, Surrey.*

A MECHANIZED QUARRY WITH KILNS AND HYDRATING PLANT

LIMESTONE
AS A RAW MATERIAL IN INDUSTRY

LIMESTONE

AS A RAW MATERIAL
IN
INDUSTRY

BY

F. P. STOWELL
B.Sc., Ph.D., F.R.I.C.

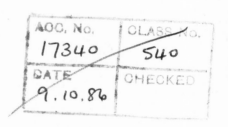

Published under the auspices of
IMPERIAL CHEMICAL INDUSTRIES LTD.

OXFORD UNIVERSITY PRESS
LONDON NEW YORK TORONTO
1963

Oxford University Press, Amen House, London E.C.4

GLASGOW   NEW YORK   TORONTO   MELBOURNE   WELLINGTON
BOMBAY   CALCUTTA   MADRAS   KARACHI   LAHORE   DACCA
CAPE TOWN   SALISBURY   NAIROBI   IBADAN   ACCRA
KUALA LUMPUR   HONG KONG

Printed in Great Britain

PREFACE

This book has been prepared by Imperial Chemical Industries Limited, with the assistance of The Science Masters' Association and The Association of Women Science Teachers, to bridge the gap between the chemistry learned at school and that same chemistry as it is applied in industrial practice. It describes the getting of limestone, the manufacture of limestone products and their uses in industry. Limestone is not a pure chemical, but a mineral consisting of calcium carbonate associated with varying proportions of impurities. Its behaviour, therefore, follows that of calcium carbonate, but always modified by the physical and chemical effects of these impurities, which vary not only from one type or class of limestone to another but within the type itself. In consequence, readers of this book will find that, whereas the chemistry of pure calcium carbonate is the key to our understanding of the manufacture and uses of lime products, the whole technology is influenced to a remarkable degree by the physical nature of the limestone and the impurities in it.

The author gratefully acknowledges the help he has received from his colleagues in the preparation of this book.

CONTENTS

LIST OF PLATES

INTRODUCTION

Limestone in its various forms is a mineral consisting mainly of calcium carbonate, associated with mineral impurities such as silica, iron oxide, alumina, magnesium carbonate and calcium sulphate. Also present are traces of other metallic oxides and carbonates, but in quantities usually too minute to be of concern in any but the most specialized industrial processes.

On calcination, limestone is decomposed into carbon dioxide gas and *quicklime*. The latter consists of calcium oxide, together with the non-volatile impurities originally associated with the lime-stone, and possibly others picked up, in traces, from the fuel used for calcination.

Quicklime combines with water with the evolution of heat to form *slaked lime*, the main constituent of which is calcium hydroxide. In excess of water, a little of the hydroxide dissolves, but the bulk remains in suspension, giving *milk of lime*, the form in which limestone products are used for many industrial operations. When milk of lime is allowed to stand, it thickens up to *lime putty*, in which form it is used for plastering and for building mortar.

The process of slaking and running to a milk or putty on site is rather dirty and laborious. Quicklime, moreover, deteriorates rapidly on keeping. Many users, therefore, prefer *hydrated lime*, which is a fine powder made by the lime manufacturer, by slaking specially selected quicklime under scientifically controlled conditions and purifying the product by air-classification. Hydrated lime keeps indefinitely without serious deterioration, and, on mixing with water, gives a correspondingly pure milk of lime.

Limestone itself was probably employed in the Stone Age, but there are definite records of its use in the Egyptian Second Dynasty. Lucas mentions its use in the Giza Pyramids. Lime was known to the Romans, not only for building, but for many other purposes, including medicine. The importance of purity was stressed by Pliny the Elder in his 'Chapters on Chemical Subjects', in which he describes the production, slaking and uses of lime.

The use of limestone and lime in building spread rapidly throughout

1

Europe in the fifteenth century. Systematic investigation of lime and its properties gradually showed how important it was, and could be, to the industrial life of the country. As the most easily available and lowest-cost alkali, it came to play a fundamental part in numerous industrial processes. This part is still growing as the country's economy expands.

Chapter I
LIMESTONE

Origin

Calcium carbonate is one of the commonest and most widely occurring minerals in the earth's crust, and the term limestone includes all rocks which consist chiefly of calcium carbonate. Limestones are mainly of marine origin, with the exception of occasional thin freshwater deposits, beds of chemically precipitated limestones and vein deposits of crystalline calcium carbonate.

The earliest forms of igneous rocks contained calcium salts, which gradually dissolved and reached the oceans, where they furnished the material for the skeletal matter of minute organisms existing on the ocean beds. This was compacted under pressure, forming limestone, which is essentially a sedimentary clastic rock. Evidence of its formation from the remains of marine organisms can frequently be seen in the form of fossils which are exposed on weathered surfaces of the rock.

In the course of time, earth movements and folding raised the ocean beds to form mountain ranges, and subsequent erosion of the shale and grit cover in many areas exposed the limestone masses.

Limestone deposits are very widely distributed throughout the world, and space permits only a consideration of their occurrence in the British Isles, in which they are found in nearly all systems of rocks from the Pre-Cambrian to the Tertiary periods. The purest originate from the ocean beds farthest from the land masses, where, in addition, very little sandy and silty material was deposited from fast-flowing rivers. Of particular interest, for example, is the deposit which coincided with, or just preceded, the laying down of the coal measures, and which is known as carboniferous limestone, bands of which, of very high purity, are found in the Buxton, North-West Yorkshire, South Wales and Bristol areas.

Solubility of calcium carbonate

The familiar experiment in which the bubbling of carbon dioxide through lime water produces at first a precipitate of calcium carbonate, which the continued passage of the gas redissolves, shows the need for careful definition of conditions in speaking of the solubility of calcium carbonate.

If calcium carbonate is added to water in the absence of a gaseous phase, minute quantities of calcium and carbonate ions pass into solution—at equilibrium the Ca^{2+} and CO_3^{2-} activities are such that the activity solubility product S_{CaCO_3} is $4 \cdot 8 \times 10^{-9}$ at 25° C.

The carbonate ion, however, is concerned with the following equilibria:

$$CO_3^{2-} + H^+ \rightleftharpoons HCO_3^-$$
$$HCO_3^- + H^+ \rightleftharpoons H_2CO_3$$

and since the concentration of the undissociated carbonic acid is affected by that of the dissolved carbon dioxide, the concentration of calcium, carbonate and bicarbonate ions in those cases in which the solutions are in contact with the atmosphere varies according to the partial pressure of carbon dioxide (Table 1).

TABLE 1

Solubility of Calcium Carbonate in Aqueous Solutions of Carbon Dioxide at 25° C

CO_2 partial pressure (atm)	Millimoles calcium per kg water	Millimoles bicarbonate per kg water
0·00031	0·52	1·02
0·00038	0·56	1·10
0·00093	0·76	1·50
0·00334	1·17	2·32
0·00690	1·51	3·01
0·0160	2·01	4·01
0·0432	2·87	5·74
0·1116	4·03	8·06
0·9684	8·91	17·82

The lowest partial pressure quoted is approximately that in ordinary air.

It will be observed that the composition of the solutions approximates to calcium bicarbonate, and that if the atmosphere over the solutions becomes richer in carbon dioxide, calcium carbonate will be dissolved. Conversely if the carbon dioxide content of the atmosphere is reduced, calcium carbonate will be precipitated. Changes in temperature, by changing the solubility of carbon dioxide in the solution, will also have an

4

effect in the solution and dissolution of calcium carbonate in water in contact with atmosphere containing carbon dioxide. It is these factors which are responsible for the remarkable natural phenomena encountered in the limestone country of the Peak district of Derbyshire, the Cheddar district of Somerset, and certain areas of north-west Yorkshire—the fissures, underground rivers, lakes and the caverns which are famed for the grotesque beauty of the stalactites and stalagmites found in them.

Classification

The concentration of the impurities in limestone has a marked effect on its subsequent physical and chemical behaviour. In the strict geological sense, limestones are classified according to their age, but unless a detailed study is made of the conditions under which they were laid down, it is extremely difficult to predict their chemical composition, and very often the most practical approach is to classify them from the properties and behaviour of the quicklime or hydrated lime manufactured from them, but always remembering that there is no sharp line of demarcation in the chemical sense.

As outlined in the introduction, limestone consists of calcium oxide in combination with carbon dioxide, and it also contains varying amounts of silica, iron oxide, alumina, sulphate and magnesia. On calcination, these non-volatile impurities are not only retained in the resulting quicklime but are concentrated roughly in the ratio 100:56, as is obvious from the simple equation of decomposition:

$$CaCO_3 \rightarrow CaO + CO_2 \uparrow \text{ gas}$$

$CaCO_3$		CaO		$CO_2 \uparrow$	gas
plus non-volatile impurities		plus non-volatile impurities			
100 parts by weight	$\rightarrow$	56 parts by weight	+	44 parts by weight.	

One of the properties of the lime markedly affected by the concentrations of certain associated impurities such as silica and alumina is its *hydraulicity*, or power of setting under water. The industry chiefly concerned with this is building, but the property can be reasonably correlated with the concentration of impurities to a degree which renders the hydraulicity of a lime a broad guide to its overall purity and hence its suitability for an industrial process.

Using the hydraulicity index, limes and their parent stones fall into four main categories:

5

(i) *Non-hydraulic* (high calcium). These are the purest limes, containing up to 97% calcium oxide or over. They do not set under water, since they contain a very low concentration of silicates and aluminates, and as a logical consequence of their purity, non-hydraulic limes are eminently suitable for use in the chemical and other industries where more than traces of specific impurities are harmful.

(ii) *Semi-hydraulic*. These limes contain sufficient impurities (up to say 15%) to render them feebly or moderately hydraulic. The effect of lower calcium oxide content, coupled with higher concentration of impurities, make semi-hydraulic limes, as a class, much less suitable for use in manufacturing processes than the non-hydraulic type.

(iii) *Hydraulic*. Hydraulic, or eminently hydraulic, limes are, in fact, natural cements, the hydration of the complex silicates and aluminates present in the high concentration of impurities conferring a definite, hard set, even under water.

This type of lime is very suitable for mortar, but generally unsuitable for manufacturing processes.

(iv) *Magnesian*. A lime is generally termed 'magnesian' when the magnesium oxide content is over 5%, but the figure can rise to over 40% in the case of a true dolomitic lime. This type of lime is suitable for building and agriculture, or for the few manufacturing processes where magnesium oxide is either not deleterious or is definitely required.

Very broadly, the non-hydraulic type can be identified with carboniferous limestone, or cretaceous limestone of the white chalk variety; the semi-hydraulic with middle and lower grey chalks (which contain some argillaceous material), and some Oolitic stones; the magnesian with the Permian series; the eminently hydraulic limes with the Lias and Blue Lias limestones.

Distribution in Great Britain

The accompanying map (Fig. 1) shows the distribution of limestone in Great Britain.

Deposits of the pure non-hydraulic type are of relatively small area in Scotland and, on the whole, either inaccessible or in positions uneconomic to work. Considerable areas exist in Ireland, not largely exploited.

In England and Wales the purest (non-hydraulic) deposits are in Derbyshire (notably the Buxton area), north-west Yorkshire, Somerset and North and South Wales, with Buxton possibly topping the list for purity. The semi-hydraulic types are scattered, but perhaps most concentrated as chalky stone in South-East England, where the white chalk calcium carbonate is also mainly encountered. The chalks vary in purity from, say, 65%–80% CaCO₃ to as high as 96%.

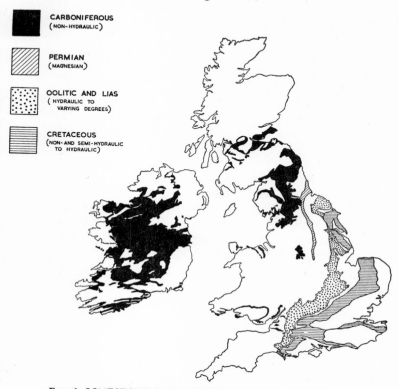

CARBONIFEROUS
(NON-HYDRAULIC)

PERMIAN
(MAGNESIAN)

OOLITIC AND LIAS
(HYDRAULIC TO
VARYING DEGREES)

CRETACEOUS
(NON- AND SEMI-HYDRAULIC
TO HYDRAULIC)

FIG. 1. LIMESTONE DISTRIBUTION IN GREAT BRITAIN
AND EIRE

The eminently hydraulic types are to be found mainly in East Anglia and in a band from there to Devonshire, while magnesian limestones exist in a strip stretching roughly from the north-east coast to Nottinghamshire.

Quarrying

Quarrying concerns the winning of the stone from the virgin deposits. The choice of a site for a quarry, lime-burning and lime-hydrating plant must obviously depend on the proximity of suitable stone of uniform

7

quality, but a further factor to be borne in mind is the ready accessibility of transport to the markets where the products are to be sold.

Blasting and getting

The first main step in 'winning' or 'getting' limestone is blasting (Plate 1), but before this can begin any top soil must be removed from the rock so that the blasted stone will be contaminated as little as possible.

Primary blasting is then carried out to separate the stone from the parent rock. Various methods are in existence, but the most up to date is well-drill blasting. Vertical holes are sunk in the rock mass behind and parallel to the quarry face, the holes filled with high explosive and the charge fired electrically. The number of well-drill holes, the distance behind the face, and the quantity and disposition of the explosive charge depend on the quantity of stone to be gotten and the optimum degree of fragmentation required. A number of other factors also enter which call for expert survey and calculation before a successful blast can be carried out. Depending on requirements, primary blasts of this type can release anything from 30,000 to 250,000 tons of stone per blast. Very roughly $4\frac{1}{2}$ tons of stone will be gotten per lb of explosive.

After the blast, the bulk of the stone now lying at the quarry face is ready for transport to the crushing and grinding plant. In an up-to-date quarry it is picked up by mechanical shovels (Plate 2) and loaded into diesel quarry vehicles which run as a continuous service between quarry face and crushing plant (Plate 3). If calculations on fragmentation have been efficient, very little of the stone is too large for loading; but if so, the lumps in question are reduced in size by secondary blasting.

Crushing, grading and cleaning

The stone has now to be crushed, cleaned and reduced to the desired sizes for the various industries in which it is required. The cleaning of the stone is much less important if its uses are limited to, say, agriculture and building when burnt to lime, but if the product is to be used in a manufacturing process, as in the case of the non-hydraulic type, the reduction of impurities to a minimum is essential.

The diesel quarry vehicles are driven to the crushing and grading plant, which houses primary and secondary crushers, washing plants and screens. The stone is tipped into a primary crusher, whence it passes to the first screens. If necessary, any oversize can be withdrawn and recrushed.

The problem of cleaning then arises. The limestone, as quarried, con-

1. A WELL-DRILL BLAST

2. A MECHANICAL SHOVEL IN ACTION

3. QUARRY VEHICLES IN ACTION

tains two kinds of impurities (*a*) those inherent in the stone itself, (*b*) adventitious impurities derived from possible silt or clay 'faults' between the limestone beds or disposed in vertical cracks in the deposit. These adventitious impurities, or contaminants, can be reduced to a minimum by washing the crushed stone.

The washed stone is then further screened into the sizes required by industry, including lime burning, and conveyed into hoppers, silos or other compartments in the crushing plant from which it can, as required, be loaded into rail or road wagons for transport to the consumer.

Grinding

For some purposes limestone is required in a pulverized or ground form. Part of the quarried stone is diverted to another plant, where it is dried and ground in suitable mills. The product is usually sold in a range of grades of fineness, which can be achieved by alteration in grinding time or load, or by air screening.

Transport

Lump limestone is usually sold loose in bulk, while ground stone is marketed either loose or in paper or hessian bags. Both lump and ground stone can be conveyed in rail or road containers, with simple precautions to protect the ground form from rain.

Chapter II

CONVERSION OF LIMESTONE TO QUICKLIME

Chemistry

The chemistry of lime burning appears at first sight to be simple, the principles being expressed by the equation for the dissociation of calcium carbonate by heat:

$CaCO_3$	$\rightleftharpoons$	CaO	$+$	CO_2
Calcium		Calcium		Carbon
Carbonate		Oxide		Dioxide.

The physical chemistry of this classic reaction in a closed system has been the subject of much study. The system consists of two components in three phases, and is therefore univariant. It is a simple instance of heterogeneous reaction, there is no tendency to form solid solutions with pure calcium carbonate, and it is generally accepted that the increase in dissociation pressure with temperature is regular (Fig. 2).

It may legitimately be assumed that calcium carbonate and calcium oxide possess definite vapour pressures and that the heterogeneous equilibrium is dependent on the equilibrium between the substances in the gaseous state. Treated in this way, it may be regarded as homogeneous, and the law of mass action applied thus:

$$\frac{p_1 \times p_2}{p_3} = kp$$

where p_1, p_2 and p_3 are the partial pressures of carbon dioxide, calcium oxide and calcium carbonate respectively. So long as solid oxide and carbonate are present, however, p_2 and p_3 must be constant, and thus p_1, the pressure of carbon dioxide, be constant, at a given temperature. When (as in the case of lime burning) the reaction is in an open system, it can proceed to completion when p_1 is equal to, or exceeds, 1 atmosphere. Various values are quoted in the literature, from laboratory determinations, of the temperature of decomposition of pure calcium carbonate, the most acceptable being in the neighbourhood of 900° C.

Since the experimental values of the dissociation pressures increase with rise of temperature, the principle of Le Chatelier requires that the reaction should be endothermic. The heat absorbed per mole of carbon dioxide formed can be calculated by the van't Hoff isochore, to give a value of 39,460 calories. Using pure calcite, probably the most reliable experimental figure is 42,600 calories at 25° C.

We have seen, therefore, that, in an open system, 1 mole of pure calcium carbonate will decompose at a temperature in the neighbourhood of 900° C,

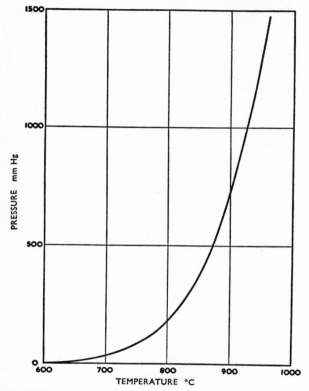

FIG. 2. DISSOCIATION PRESSURES OF CALCIUM CARBONATE

by the application of approximately 43,000 calories of heat, the pressure of carbon dioxide equalling 1 atmosphere. Similarly, in the case of lime-burning, a fixed quantity of heat is required to convert 1 ton of limestone to lime, but not in the same exact ratio. Limestone is not pure calcium carbonate, atmospheric pressure varies, and the partial pressure of carbon dioxide in the decomposing mass within a lime kiln is variable. There is the contribution of the same gas from the fuel used in burning. It is obvious that one of the major factors in the efficiency of the reaction under practical lime-burning conditions must therefore be the removal of carbon dioxide by adequate forced or induced draught.

There is also definite evidence that the temperature of decomposition varies with the physical nature of the calcium carbonate.

With limestone, the heat in a lime kiln is supplied from fuel, which may be coal or coke, mixed with the limestone burden, producer gas from an external source, or natural gas if available, as in certain areas, notably in the U.S.A.

As we have seen in Chapter I, limestone contains certain inherent non-volatile impurities. On conversion of the stone to lime it can be deduced from the equation of the reaction that these impurities will be concentrated *roughly* in the ratio of 100:56. In addition, impurities in the fuel can be picked up by the lime, by absorption and reaction if volatile, or by contact and reaction if non-volatile. Any adventitious impurities, as contaminants on the stone, may react similarly. It follows logically that pure clean stone is a necessity in the manufacture of limes of high chemical quality, and the choice of fuel should be the subject of skilled analytical and scientific control.

It has been found that the presence of iron, alumina and other impurities during calcination markedly affects the rate of hydration of the resulting quicklime and the reactivity of the calcium hydroxide formed. If the temperature of calcination has been high enough to allow mobility of the calcium oxide to bring about crystal growth, it will also permit impurities to move to the grain boundaries. A reduction in surface energy results, causing a layer of impurities on the calcium oxide crystals. On subsequent attempted hydration, there may then be absorption of a water layer at the surface without uniform reaction, the latter being limited to those spots on the surface not marked by impurities.

Apart, therefore, from the refinements of cleaning the stone, a high degree of technical control in burning, and skill in sorting the resulting lime, a minimum of inherent impurities in the original limestone is desirable if the lime produced is to be satisfactory for an exacting industrial process.

Effect of further heat on the properties of quicklime

Apart from the obvious precautions which must be taken to ensure the highest possible chemical purity of lime produced for the more demanding industries, it is with the properties of lime resulting from its physical condition, if it may so be termed, that the major problems of efficient lime burning begin. Most modern kilns have accurate control of temperature and draught, and are fed with graded stone, but, in spite of this, it is impossible to ensure that each individual lump of limestone receives identical heat treatment. Further, since the decomposition of a lump proceeds from the outside to the interior, the surface is converted to lime first, and this lime is, in consequence, exposed to heat, after formation, for a much longer period than that in the centre of the lump.

During decomposition the calcium carbonate particles retain their rhomboid shape and the calcium oxide particles formed are built up of cubic crystals resulting from the destruction of the space lattice of the original calcium carbonate crystal during heating, followed by recrystallization. The small calcium oxide crystals then aggregate to form pseudomorphs of the original calcium carbonate particles from which they resulted. The constituent crystals are separated by pores resulting from the elimination of carbon dioxide from the space lattice of the original calcium carbonate. The occupied space in the calcium oxide cell is only 43% of that in the calcium carbonate cell. In other words 57% of the calcium oxide produced under ideal conditions would consist of voids. The spaces between the cells are several times wider than a water molecule and hence such a material would be extremely reactive to water.

Continued heating has the effect of narrowing the internal free spaces. Though the unit cells of calcium oxide do not apparently alter in size or shape, they aggregate into larger crystals. The pores dilate and decrease in number, and the voids between particles decrease in size. The passage of water molecules is restricted and, even when this has been achieved, the available area at which reaction can commence is small. Expressed simply, the lime becomes progressively denser and less reactive through recrystallization and this loss in reactivity is transmitted to the milk of lime resulting from subsequent slaking. This, in turn, will obviously affect the industrial process in which the lime is used (see Chapter III and IV). The calcium oxide will also enter into solid solution with the impurities.

Although there are certain processes which do not call for the lime to be slaked, or which are less sensitive to reactivity in the milk, and which can, in consequence, utilize run-of-kiln lime, hand sorting or picking of the burnt lime is the logical sequence to lime burning for use in very many industrial processes. It is a highly skilled operation.

Recarbonation

We have seen that in a lime kiln, provided the carbon dioxide is removed efficiently, the reaction

$$CaCO_3 \rightarrow CaO + CO_2 \uparrow$$

should proceed to completion at the requisite temperature. If, however, the partial pressure of carbon dioxide builds up sufficiently, the reverse reaction can take place, and the rate is at a maximum at temperatures in the neighbourhood of 650° C. Since the newly converted hot lime, originally at a temperature of roughly 1100° C (see later), must be cooled before being drawn from a kiln, it must pass through a zone where it attains this temperature of 650° C for a period as the burden sinks slowly through the kiln to the drawing eyes. Care must therefore be taken to guard against back-concentrations of carbon dioxide in the cooling zone of the kiln.

Lime kilns

There are numerous types of lime kilns in Great Britain, with capacities as diverse as their *modus operandi*. In the earliest types of kiln, known as 'intermittent', the raw materials necessary for lime burning, limestone and fuel, were charged into a pit and the fuel lighted. When the mass had burnt out the lime was picked out by hand. A later modification, still to be seen in some districts, was the first 'continuous' kiln, which consisted of a vertical shaft in a cliff face, lined with refractory bricks and equipped with apertures at the base of the shaft. Limestone and coal or coke were fed to the lighted kiln from the top and lime drawn from the apertures at the base. As the level at the top fell it was restored by replenishments of fuel and stone, so that the process could roughly be described as continuous.

During the last half-century research has been devoted to the technique of lime burning, coupled with vast strides in kiln design and operation. In most modern kilns more accurate control has been taken of the burning and the lime is drawn under greatly improved conditions for the workers.

Broadly speaking, modern kilns fall into three main classes.

(i) Vertical shaft kilns, into which the stone is fed at the top and the lime drawn from the bottom. These may again be subdivided into mixed-feed, gas-fired, and patent or Spencer type kilns, depending on the method of introducing the fuel and similar modifications in operation. The capacity of shaft kilns may range from outputs of say 30–40 tons per week, in the case of the older types, to 800–1000 tons per week from larger modern kilns, normally operated in batteries.

(ii) Horizontal kilns, which consist of a series of chambers arranged in the form of an ellipse or ring. The fire burning the lime travels slowly round the kiln, being controlled by a system of flues. Limestone is stacked in front of the fire, and lime drawn from behind it. This type of kiln, with outputs of up to 600 tons per week, is expensive in labour and is now almost non-existent.

14

(iii) Rotary kilns (Plate 4). These are sloping rotating cylinders lined with refractory bricks, into the upper end of which graded limestone is charged. This slowly falls the length of the kiln by gravity and is exposed to the source of heat introduced from burners at the lower end, where the resulting lime falls into coolers and thence to storage. The fuel may be pulverized coal, gas or oil.

The output of this type of kiln naturally depends on its size and method of operation, but is of the order of up to 1000–1400 tons per week.

All types of kilns, whether of brick, stone, concrete or steel, are lined with refractory material, which must be carefully chosen, since it must withstand both abrasion and chemical attack at high temperatures. It is impossible, within the scope of this book, to describe the operation of such kilns in detail, so that the general principle of the process in a typical shaft kiln only is outlined. Figure 3 is not to scale, and is simplified purely to illustrate the broad principles.

The ancillary gear may include equipment for recording the temperature of the exit gases and the concentration of carbon dioxide in them, the temperature of the limestone and lime burden at predetermined levels in

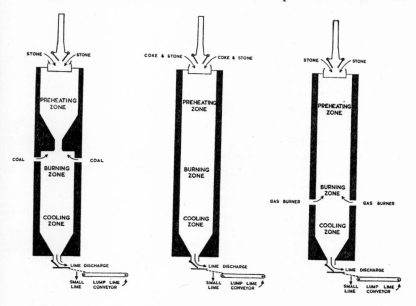

Fig. 3. THE SIMPLE PRINCIPLES OF SHAFT KILN OPERATION

15

the kiln, draught adjustment and burning zone level control, and numerous other refinements, details of which obviously cannot be given here.

A kiln may arbitrarily be divided into a pre-heating zone, a burning zone and a cooling zone. The limestone is fed to the kiln through charging-doors at the top. The fuel may be either mixed with it or introduced through inlets or doors lower in the shaft. As lime is drawn from the bottom of the kiln, the limestone at the top gradually sinks through the pre-heating zone into the burning zone, the temperature of the burden increasing to about 1100° C–1200° C.

In this zone the conversion to lime is completed, the partial pressure of the carbon dioxide exceeding atmospheric, and the gas removed by natural or reinforced draught. It will be patent to the reader that the more efficient the pre-heating and the carbon dioxide removal, and the evenness of temperature in the burning zone, the higher the overall efficiency of the process. Heat losses by radiation should be minimized and the temperature of the exit gases maintained at a working minimum.

After conversion into lime, the charge passes down through the cooling zone to the drawing eyes, where, in a properly controlled kiln, it will be drawn at or very little above atmospheric temperature, and graded and hand-picked. The whole process is, of course, continuous.

Grades of burnt lime—sorting or hand picking

Non-hydraulic lime which has been burnt at the lowest practicable temperature with the minimum of heat treatment is relatively light and porous, white in colour and extremely reactive. Since this type of lime is required for the majority of subsequent industrial processes (there are exceptions, as will be seen later), the ideal would be a kiln output of practically all this grade.

But, as stated earlier, the dissociation of any individual lump of lime-stone to lime proceeds continuously from exterior to interior, and it is impossible to convert the centre to lime without extra heat treatment of the lime nearer the surface of the lump, and we have already noted the adverse effect of this. The obvious solution would be to speed up the reaction in order to reduce the period of after heat treatment to a minimum, were it not for the fact that this would necessitate higher temperatures. Since it is the *quantity* of heat applied which is the main controlling factor, higher temperature, even for a shorter time, could have an equally adverse effect on the physical quality of the lime. To achieve a satisfactory compromise requires skill and experience, backed by rigid technical con-

16

trol, and it will be seen that the production of lime of purity and satisfactory physical quality, in the correct balance for the exacting requirements of modern industry, is not as simple a matter as might appear at first sight.

A kiln will therefore produce a mixture of the very reactive lime (known as 'light-burnt') and the denser grade (known as 'solid-burnt), the proportions of the two depending on the requirements of the industries for which the lime is being burnt. The size of the lumps will be fixed by that of the original stone, which in turn is decided by the type of kiln being used.

In addition to the 'lump lime', there is a certain quantity of smaller material resulting from the abrasion of the larger lumps in passage through the kiln, and a few pieces with unburnt stone cores, arising from incomplete conversion of the lump to lime.

The kiln output as it stands, known as 'run-of-kiln lime', is first passed over a jigging screen to remove the undersize, together with any cinders or clinker. This undersize is known as 'small lime' and is suitable for agriculture, mortar (if properly treated) and other uses where high CaO content and purity are not vital. In a modern plant the larger lump material then passes along picking belts, where skilled operatives remove the pieces with stone cores (known in the trade as 'bullheads') and sort the remainder into light-burnt and solid-burnt lump lime. These grades are usually known as 'Best Hand Picked' or 'B.H.P.' lime. For a few industries where reactivity and colour are of paramount necessity, the very lightest, best lumps are picked from the light-burnt B.H.P. grade and are designated 'Specially Selected' lime.

The picked product then passes either direct into road or rail containers or into loading hoppers, to be collected later. Some may be packed into drums for export, while a specially selected quantity of the light-burnt grade will be conveyed to the hydrating plant (see Chapter III).

Transport and storage

Calcium oxide is extremely hygroscopic. It follows, therefore, that the higher the calcium oxide content of a lime, the more quickly will it deteriorate. In the case of the hydraulic limes the absorption of moisture from the atmosphere is slow, but the rate increases progressively through the semi-hydraulic to the type with highest oxide content, the non-hydraulic. This type reacts violently with liquid water, and picks up atmospheric moisture very rapidly, to fall into a fine white powder. This in turn absorbs atmospheric carbon dioxide. Atmospheric moisture enters through the

17

pores of the lump and the expansion accompanying hydration breaks the lump, exposing fresh surface and consequent access to moisture and carbon dioxide. Eventually the larger portion of the lump falls to a powdery mixture of carbonated material which is relatively inactive—known in the trade as fallen or air-slaked lime. This absorption process is accompanied by the evolution of heat (see Chapter III). If by chance the process is accelerated by the intrusion of liquid water, the temperature of the mass can become high enough to set even thick wooden containers (such as railway wagons) on fire.

It follows that the transport of quicklime calls for thought. If the material is transported in open containers, such as railway wagons or lorries, they should be well covered with sheets of the tarpaulin type to protect the load from rain. Transport should be as quick as possible to prevent deterioration through air-slaking. This is even more imperative in the summer, because although (statistically) there is less chance of rain, the atmosphere is more humid.

It might be argued that airtight containers should be used for the transport of quicklime, but it must be remembered that lime is a low-priced commodity and, although a few users adopt this type of container, the majority rely on sheeted railway wagons or lorries.

The question of storage presents similar problems. The best solution of the difficulty is suggested in Chapter III, but should it be decided to store the quicklime as such, it should be kept in a metal or concrete building, i.e. of non-inflammable type, on a concrete floor as dry and free from draughts as possible. It should not be stored near boilers or furnaces, however, because it will readily pick up any carbon dioxide or sulphur fumes. Further, the material should be stored in such a manner that rapid turn-over in consumption can be effected.

Chapter III

CONVERSION OF QUICKLIME TO SLAKED
OR HYDRATED LIME

Chemistry

Calcium oxide reacts with water in accordance with the following equation:

CaO	+	H_2O	$\rightarrow$	$Ca(OH)_2$
Calcium Oxide		Water		Calcium Hydroxide
(quicklime)				(slaked or hydrated lime)
56 pts by wt	+	18 pts by wt	$\rightarrow$	74 pts by wt.

The reaction is exothermic, 15,500 cal being evolved per mole of reactant at 20° C. The rate of reaction of quicklime with liquid water is modified by its physical state (grade of burning) and the amount of impurities it contains. The pure, non-hydraulic type, if lightly-burnt, reacts with violence, the reaction rate becoming slower the more solidly-burnt the lime. Semi-hydraulic limes slake more slowly than the non-hydraulic, while with eminently hydraulic lime it is necessary to use a minimum of water and to conserve the heat to induce the reaction to proceed. Magnesian limes are unique in that the rates of reaction with water of both calcium oxide and magnesium oxide are factors to take into account, with the result that this type slakes in two stages.

Numerous theories have been put forward to explain the mechanism of hydration, but one of the most feasible suggests that the hydration units are not the gross particles of lime, but the small crystals making up these particles. The reaction begins at one or more crystals of calcium oxide to form a nucleus of calcium hydroxide. The conversion of the mass of the particle into hydroxide then proceeds at the expanding boundary between hydroxide and unchanged oxide. The passage of water to the inner unreacted portions can occur either by diffusion through the open spaces between the particles of calcium hydroxide or by adsorption on the calcium hydroxide followed by diffusion along its surface.

During hydration, the cubic calcium oxide cells are converted into four

19

times the number of calcium hydroxide cells. The oxide cell contains four molecules, and the new hydroxide cell only one molecule. The four cells occupy considerably more space than the original calcium oxide cell, and there is, on hydration, a great expansion in volume and decrease in density.

It has been found that the calcium hydroxide often appears as a pseudomorph of the original calcium carbonate particle, having no birefringence and being quite different in appearance from the well-defined hexagonal crystals which can be prepared from a solution of calcium hydroxide in water. These isotropic particles sometimes disintegrate with time into smaller ones, which contain a considerable proportion of well-defined birefringent crystals.

Water-burnt lime

The reaction between calcium oxide and water vapour proceeds relatively slowly, and in the absence of carbon dioxide results in a fine powder of reactive calcium hydroxide, if carried out under isothermal conditions in the laboratory. With reactive lime in bulk, however, overheating takes place at centres where there is insufficient opportunity for the heat to disperse or escape. Temperatures above 100° C result in the formation of an inactive white gritty compound which is known in the trade as 'water-burnt lime'.

There is some evidence that this compound has the empirical formula $CaO.Ca(OH)_2$, but it may well be calcium hydroxide with nuclei of calcium oxide re-formed from it by the excess heat, since a much lower temperature is required ($\simeq$ 550° C) for the decomposition of calcium hydroxide than for that of calcium carbonate. The theory of compound formation is supported by the fact that this gritty substance is very inactive indeed, which is not the behaviour expected from a simple mixture of oxide and hydroxide. Whichever theory regarding this inactive material is correct, the important point is the prevention of its formation during storage and practical slaking, because not only is it good lime wasted, but its presence in milk of lime is definitely deleterious in many industrial processes.

Reaction of a pure light-burnt lime with liquid water is much more violent than with water vapour, and rapid and intimate contact with excess water is essential to utilize the latent heat of the latter to prevent local temperatures rising above 100° C. This would again result in the formation of water-burnt lime. The elimination of this substance is dealt with effectively in the manufacture of dry hydrated lime (see later), but in slaking quicklime on site it is well to follow closely the procedure detailed in the section dealing with this subject.

Milk of lime

Calcium hydroxide, the main constituent of slaked or hydrated lime, is only slightly soluble in water, the solution being commonly known as *lime water*. The bulk remains in suspension on admixture with excess water, and is known as *milk of lime*. Calcium hydroxide exhibits the rather uncommon feature of a fall in solubility with rise in temperature. At 0° C the figure is approximately 0·14 g (expressed as CaO) per 100 g solution, whereas at 100° C it is only 0·05 g. There is considerable evidence that water combines with the calcium hydroxide molecule in milks to form hydrated colloidal micelles of the type $[Ca(OH)_2 \, nH_2O]_x$. This water is held in loose combination, and is directly available, if required, in certain reactions in which lime milks are employed, such as the hydration of collagen in the dehairing and plumping of hides in the tanning industry. Here again, the higher the calcium oxide content of the original lime, and the more lightly burnt it is, the greater the degree of hydration of the calcium hydroxide micelle. The slow rate of settling of the particles in a milk of lime—a very important factor in many industrial reactions—depends not only on their size, but on their density in comparison with the surrounding medium, water, and the greater the combination, or absorption, of water by the calcium hydroxide micelles the less the relative density of the particle in that medium.

As would be expected, slaked semi-hydraulic and eminently hydraulic limes, containing lower concentrations of calcium hydroxide and less micelle formation, have less reactivity and quicker settling in milks for similar grades of burning.

Lime putty

When milk of lime is allowed to stand, progressively more water is absorbed by the agglomerates of calcium hydroxide and held in what can perhaps best be described as a colloidal sponge-like structure or gel, the mass thickening up to a putty. This putty is viscous and plastic, the water being retained tenaciously and it forms the basis of lime plastering mixes in the building trade.

The property of greater water absorption in milks exhibited by the non-hydraulic or high calcium limes is enhanced to an even more marked degree in the putties. The subject will be dealt with in greater detail in Chapter IV, when the building industry is discussed.

The effect of the degree of burning of the quicklime on the properties of milks and putties

It has been noted that solid-burnt lime is denser and less reactive to water than the lightly-burnt grade, because the crystallites of CaO in the space lattices of solid-burnt lime are larger, and therefore present less surface for reaction. This, coupled with lower porosity of the mass as a whole, results in loss of reactivity and consequent slower slaking rate (Fig. 4).

Owing to the high degree of water absorption of the micelles, milks from lightly-burnt limes settle very slowly, and the settled solids are light and bulky, retaining a high proportion of water (Fig. 5). On the other hand, milks from solid-burnt lime are composed of denser particles of lower micelle hydration, which settle much more quickly, and to a dense compact

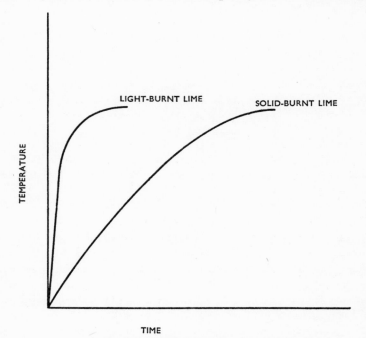

FIG. 4. SLAKING CURVES OF TYPICAL LIGHT- AND
SOLID-BURNT LIMES

mass. The milks from the lightly-burnt lime exhibit greater chemical reactivity, and are utilized in most industries.

If the calcium oxide particles possess the voids obtained during ideal decomposition (see Chapter II) there will be enough spaces for the calcium hydroxide to expand into during slaking. If, however, the lime is solidly

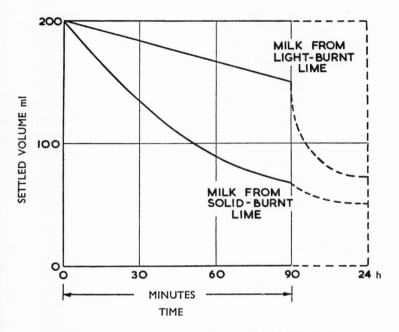

FIG. 5. SETTLING CURVES OF MILKS FROM TYPICAL LIGHT- AND SOLID-BURNT LIMES

burnt and the voids reduced, the hydroxide will have greater difficulty in expanding, and there will be, in consequence, closer packing of the cells, with loss in reactivity and micelle hydration. In some industrial processes, however, where speed of settling or of filtration is essential, some sacrifice in reactivity is made, and the more solidly-burnt lime used.

To summarize, it has been shown that the higher the CaO content of a quicklime, the lower the impurities and the more lightly it is burnt, the slower-settling and more reactive the milk of lime resulting from it, and the greater the yield of lime putty. The impact of these physical properties

23

on the suitability of a type of lime for a particular industrial process is elaborated in Chapter IV.

Slaking on site

Since the great majority of industrial processes in which lime is used involve the preparation of a milk or putty as a starting-point, it follows that the operation of slaking is generally the first task which a user is called upon to perform.

On the face of it, lime slaking seems such a simple operation that the type of man detailed to carry it out is often (though not always) of limited intelligence, and having done this work all his life, probably incorrectly, he will not believe there is a better method. The fault does not always lie at this level, either. The writer has seen mechanical slakers in action which were the result of considerable ingenuity, but of little or no knowledge of lime, its properties and behaviour. Perhaps the explanation of this aberration could best be summed up by the analogy of underrating an opponent!

As we have seen, the physical state of the lime has a considerable effect, not only on its reactivity with water, but on the subsequent reactivity and behaviour of the calcium hydroxide particles. The advantage of using the best grade of lime is nullified, however, if the lime is incorrectly or carelessly slaked. Following the research findings on the effect of calcium oxide concentration, 'heat-history', and hydration of quicklime on the calcium hydroxide micelle, further work was obviously called for on the best methods of bulk slaking within the bounds of economic practicability. These are given below, that for the non-hydraulic or high-calcium type being given in greatest detail because of the vast preponderance of its use in industry.

The three types of lime which we classified by their hydraulic indices fall broadly into the same order in rate of slaking—quick, medium and slow. The magnesian type slakes in two stages.

The best method of slaking the *non-hydraulic or high-calcium type* is rapid and intimate contact with excess water in the neighbourhood of 90° C–100° C. By this method the danger of local overheating (with consequent formation of 'water-burnt' lime) is minimized, and maximum opportunity is given for the calcium hydroxide micelles to absorb, or adsorb, water.

This temperature is both easy to attain and to judge in practice. If hot water is not available to commence with, the heat required may be obtained from the heat of reaction of the first batch of lime treated. The slaking vessel should be filled with water to a depth of 1 foot. Enough lime should be added to the water (NOT *vice versa*) to cover the bottom of the vessel and come about half-way to the surface. Stirring, hoeing (or agitation by steam, but still with stirring), should begin at once, but no lime must be allowed to rise and remain exposed above water. A plentiful supply of water should always be to hand.

The mass will begin to boil gently. Directly the escape of steam becomes too violent, or lime shows above the surface through piling up or swelling, more water should immediately be added, the idea always being to obtain a milk at temperature in the neighbourhood of 100° C. All the time the milk should be thoroughly stirred and the lime turned over.

As the mix thickens, more water should be added. Lime and water should then be added alternately, with constant stirring, till the requisite quantity of milk is obtained.

When all reaction has ceased it is important to continue stirring for at least 5 minutes, in order to ensure rapid and intimate contact between the newly-formed calcium hydroxide and the water.

The milk should be passed through a grid or sieve to remove any unburnt stone cores from the original quicklime, and any of the latter possibly left unslaked. An examination of the residue will also show whether it contains an undue proportion of the white gritty material, somewhat resembling crushed porcelain—'water-burnt' lime. If so, the slaking process has been inefficient.

We have already stated that milk of lime, if of sufficiently high calcium hydroxide concentration, will thicken up to lime putty at this stage, if left undisturbed. Care should therefore be taken to dilute the milk to below 20% hydroxide if it is to be allowed to stand in pipes in the process circuit.

For smaller users it is comparatively easy to contrive a relatively efficient slaking unit, but the treatment of large bulk quantities of quicklime calls for careful design and experience. It is wise to consult the lime manufacturer who, if up-to-date and progressive, will have a technical service department to advise, and also to put the user in touch with firms making efficient slaking units.

Semi-hydraulic limes cover the range of purity between the non-hydraulic and truly hydraulic types, with no well-defined lines of demarcation. The same applies to the rate of slaking. If the CaO content is sufficiently high, say 85%–90%, the method of slaking given above for the non-hydraulic type can be adopted without modification. If, however, the lime is found, on test, to be medium to slow slaking, common sense will dictate the amount of water to be added per batch increment, and whether heat of reaction must be dissipated or conserved.

Eminently hydraulic lime is used only for mortar or coarse stuff for plastering and is not run to a milk or putty. The heat of reaction must be conserved as much as possible during slaking. The lime should be heaped, lumps over 6 inches in size broken down, and water thrown or sprayed on the mass, making sure that each piece of lime is wetted. Only sufficient water should be added to slake the lime and allow for loss by evaporation.

The heap should then be covered, well banked down to retain heat, and left undisturbed for not less than 36 hours. If left longer, it should be protected from getting wet in the event of rain, to prevent premature setting.

As we have noted, *magnesian limes* virtually slake in two stages, because the calcium and magnesium oxides present have different rates of reaction with water. Broadly, the lime should first be sprayed with sufficient water to saturate it, care being taken not to add more water than can be absorbed. Hot water can be used, if available, and the heat of reaction conserved as far as possible. When the lime has fallen to a powder, enough water (preferably hot) should be added gradually to bring the mix to the consistency of cream. Modifications to the method have naturally been adopted for some of the industries calling for this type of lime, and the magnesian lime manufacturer should be consulted for further details.

Storage as a milk or putty

In Chapter II the difficulties of storing quicklime were pointed out. The material deteriorates chemically because of the disintegration of the lump to powder, followed by absorption of atmospheric carbon dioxide, by the newly formed calcium hydroxide, on the very large surface area exposed. Water-burnt lime may also be formed. If, however, the lime is slaked and run to a milk or putty immediately or as soon as possible after delivery, and then left undisturbed in storage tanks till required, a thin skin of carbonate will form on the surface and protect the bulk from further deterioration. The milk or putty can then be tapped off as required.

Hydrated lime

Commercial hydrated lime is the generic or class name given to the fine dry powdered calcium hydroxide produced by the lime manufacturer and usually sold in ply-paper valved bags printed with the appropriate trade-names.

If of reputable brand, hydrated lime is manufactured from selected light-burnt quicklime by slaking in specially designed units under close technical supervision. There is a variety of such slaking units and ancillary plant in existence, with modifications by individual manufacturers which are naturally secret, so that a broad description of the process must suffice.

The quicklime is crushed or pulverized and fed into the hydrating vessel, (which can be of batch type, but normally is continuous), where it comes into contact with the correct amount of water to meet stoichiometric requirements and allow for loss as steam.

It will occur to the discriminating reader that this method of slaking is fundamentally opposed to the tenets of good practice laid down earlier in this book. This would be so were it not for the fact that the process is under rigid technical control, with special mechanical precautions to ensure rapid and intimate contact between the reactants and the reduction of local overheating to a minimum.

The crude product from the hydrators may contain small unburnt stone cores and adventitious impurities from the original quicklime, particles of unslaked lime, and a small but unavoidable amount of water-burnt lime. It passes to a series of air-classifiers, in which it is subjected to a selective air stream, which is so adjusted that the pure hydrated lime is separated by gravity from these impurities. The finished product then passes to bunkers for subsequent bagging or bulk transport.

Magnesian hydrated lime

It will be remembered that magnesian quicklime requires slaking in two stages, and a milk of lime run for mortar or plaster should be matured for about 3 months before use, to ensure complete slaking. The stone contains both calcium and magnesium carbonates, and the dissociation temperature of the latter is some 400° C lower than that of calcium carbonate at the same pressure. In consequence, the magnesium oxide present in magnesian quicklime is much more solidly burnt than the calcium oxide, and, as a result, much slower slaking. The same applies to commerical hydration. Special precautions must therefore be taken in manufacturing magnesian hydrated lime, and pressure hydration is practically the only really satisfactory solution.

Packaging, transport and storage of hydrated lime

The finished product is normally marketed in ½ cwt or 1 cwt valved paper or in hessian bags. It can be transported by road, rail or sea if

27

adequately protected from rain. At least one manufacturer has also introduced a method of bulk transport in special road vehicles, which are self-discharging by means of compressed air, delivering the hydrated lime direct into bunkers at the user end, from which it can be mechanically conveyed to the individual processes as required.

Unlike quicklime, which, as we have noted, is subject to progressive deterioration during storage, hydrated lime will keep indefinitely if left undisturbed in bags in a cool dry place free from draughts or fumes from furnaces, boilers and similar sources of contamination. If accepted in bulk it will, of course, be lodged in an air-tight silo, bin, or similar receptacle.

Preparation of milk or putty from hydrated lime

Hydrated lime, being already slaked, need only be mixed with water in the correct proportions to give milk of lime of the required concentration. No sieving is necessary, since, with a reputable product, 100% will pass 36 British Standard mesh ($\simeq$ 1/60 in) and about 94%–95% will pass 200 B.S. mesh ($\simeq$ 1/330 in). The milk is chemically identical with that produced from running quicklime on site, since it is essentially a suspension of calcium hydroxide in water.

From the physical point of view, there are one or two interesting angles. Immediately after mixing with water, the milk is quicker settling than that from quicklime slaked on site in excess water, and the putty less plastic and lower in yield, because there has been no opportunity for the calcium hydroxide to absorb water and effect a corresponding hydration of the micelles. If slow settling or high putty yield is desirable, therefore, the milk should be allowed to mature for 24–48 hours, or at least overnight, when its settling properties and putty yield will approach those of a milk direct from quicklime.

Chapter IV

INDUSTRIAL USES OF LIMESTONE, QUICKLIME, AND HYDRATED LIME

Annual consumption of limestone in Great Britain

Whereas information is more readily available on the *total* annual consumption of limestone (including chalk) in Great Britain, it is very difficult to split the figure accurately into the tonnages used by the various industries, because of certain hidden factors such as, for instance, the 'captive' tonnages used by the iron and steel industry. With reservations such as this in mind, a reasonably accurate estimate has been made, based on information from various sources, of the annual consumption by the major groups of industries in 1959, expressed as percentages of the total of 50,724,000 tons:

	Approx. %
Cement	35
Chemicals, tanning, foodstuffs, water, paper, etc.	16
Agriculture	15
Iron and steel	13
Building	2
Roadstone, ballast, aggregates	19

It will be seen that the cement industry is the largest single consumer. A wide range of silica and alumina can be tolerated in the stone or chalk, because of processing adjustments in the manufacture of the cement. Roadstone, ballast and aggregates can consume high tonnages of impure limestone so long as strength requirements are met. The physical and chemical requirements for the remaining industries are dealt with later.

The suitability for industrial uses

The importance of lime in the life of the community is not generally realized. Participating in so many fundamental processes, it enters directly or indirectly into the manufacture of practically all the commodities used in everyday life.

In deciding the suitability of any type or grade of lime or limestone for a particular process, the first thing to bear in mind is that the active principle concerned is calcium oxide, and, naturally, the higher the concentration of this active principle the better. Secondly, what impurities are deleterious to the process concerned, or its end product, and what concentrations can be tolerated? Thirdly, if lime or hydrated lime is to be used, what are the physical requirements—high reactivity, volume yield, slow or quick settling, speedy filtration? With these points in mind the prospective user must strike a balance with factors such as accessibility and price, because lime is a relatively low-priced commodity and freight costs limit its range of economic availability. Taking all these things into consideration, however, it is obvious that for the vast majority of industrial uses, the demand will be for the purer high-calcium or non-hydraulic types of lime.

Tables 2 to 6 set out the main industrial uses of limestone and lime and the type of material best suited for the purpose, with typical analyses of high-grade products.

In the previous chapters the reader has followed the basic principles of the production, for industry, of limestone, quicklime and hydrated lime, the effect of further heat treatment on freshly formed quicklime, the pitfalls of the seemingly simple operations of slaking and running to milk and putty, and the properties of hydrated lime. Let us now consider the actual uses of the products in industrial processes. For obvious reasons, great detail is impossible, but an attempt has again been made to outline the basic principles.

Agriculture and horticulture

Together with building, agriculture is one of the earliest known uses of lime and limestone. With cultivation, manuring, and the use of concentrated chemical fertilizers, liming may be considered one of the essentials in promoting land fertility.

The mechanism of the action of lime in the soil is complex. Probably its most important function is to adjust the soil to the hydrogen-ion concentration, or pH, which constitutes the best environment for the soil bacteria which convert otherwise unavailable nitrogen into a form readily assimilable by the plant. By the same mechanism, it aids the decomposition of waste vegetable matter, and by reducing acidity, it retards or even

30

prevents the development of harmful organisms which thrive in acid soils, such as the type which promote 'club-root' in the cabbage family.

Lime improves the texture of the soil and renders it more workable. In clay soils, it flocculates the colloidal particles and renders them granular, making the soil more crumbly and hence easier to dig or plough. Insoluble complexes in this type of soil, notably those containing potassium, are split up following flocculation.

Lime deficiency in the soil is revealed by the prevalence of sorrel and spurry on arable land, and coarse herbage and thin, wiry hay crops on grassland, together with weeds like plantain and sour-dock, which flourish

TABLE 2

Main Industrial Uses of Limestone and the Quality Required

Use	Properties required
Agriculture	Must be ground, composition relatively immaterial, but a statement of the neutralizing value and grading must be made under the Fertilizer and Feeding Stuffs Act, 1926.
Aggregates for concrete	Lump, graded, good crushing strength.
Asphalt	Chemical composition not of primary importance, but the stone must be ground and graded to meet the requirements of various British Standards for fillers for asphalt.
Coal mine dusting	Ground to certain grading requirements. Silica must be low.
Glass	Ground, calcium oxide high, magnesium and iron low.
Gravels, railway ballast	Graded as specified by the user. Crushing strength and abrasion resistance more important than chemical composition.
Iron and steel	Graded lump, sulphur and phosphorus low.
Soda ash	Graded lump, clean, very high purity.
Sugar	Graded lump, calcium oxide high, magnesium and sulphur low.

TABLE 3

Main Industrial Uses of Lime and the Quality of Lime Required

Industries where chemical purity, reactivity and other physical requirements are all of paramount importance	Industries where reactivity and other physical requirements are of paramount importance	Industries where minimum content of certain impurities is of paramount importance, but physical properties are immaterial within limits	Industries where chemical purity and physical properties are relatively immaterial
Carbide	Ammonia distillation	Steel	Agriculture[2]
Causticizing			Acid neutralization
Ceramics	Dehydration		Effluent treatment
Chemicals— high grade	Plastering[1]		Mortar[1]
Chlorination	Sand lime bricks		
Food stuffs	Sewage treatment		
Glue and gelatine	Water softening		
Magnesium	Wire drawing		
Organic syntheses			
Pharmacy and cosmetics			
Satin white			
Sugar			
Tanning			
Varnish			
Water treatment			

[1]Should meet the requirements of British Standard 890—*Building Limes*.
[2]A statement of the neutralizing value must be made under the Fertilizer and Feeding Stuffs Act, 1926.

TABLE 4

Typical Analysis of Pure Limestone (Non-Hydraulic) Suitable for Industrial Purposes

Constituents		%
Calcium carbonate	$CaCO_3$	98·24
Calcium sulphate	$CaSO_4$	0·14
Magnesium carbonate	$MgCO_3$	0·49
Ferric oxide	Fe_2O_3	0·07
Aluminium oxide	Al_2O_3	0·11
Silica, etc.	SiO_2	0·73
Moisture	H_2O	0·25

TABLE 5

Typical Analysis of Pure Quicklime Suitable for Industrial Purposes

(Burnt from limestone of Table 4)

Constituents		% Dry
Calcium oxide	CaO	97·14
Calcium carbonate	$CaCO_3$	0·71
Calcium sulphate	$CaSO_4$	0·49
Magnesium oxide	MgO	0·41
Ferric oxide	Fe_2O_3	0·13
Alluminium oxide	Al_2O_3	0·18
Silica, etc.	SiO_2	1·01

33

TABLE 6

Hydrated Lime Suitable for Industrial Purposes
Typical Analysis

Constituents		%
Calcium hydroxide	$Ca(OH)_2$	96·92
Calcium carbonate	$CaCO_3$	0·93
Calcium sulphate	$CaSO_4$	0·30
Magnesium hydroxide	$Mg(OH)_2$	0·45
Ferric oxide	Fe_2O_3	0·07
Aluminium oxide	Al_2O_3	0·14
Silica, etc.	SiO_2	0·53
Moisture	H_2O	0·62

Typical Grading

% passing 36 B.S. mesh (≃ 1/60 in)	100
% passing 52 B.S. mesh (≃ 1/90 in)	100
% passing 72 B.S. mesh (≃ 1/120 in)	99·9
% passing 100 B.S. mesh (≃ 1/170 in)	99·5
% passing 150 B.S. mesh (≃ 1/250 in)	97·2
% passing 200 B.S. mesh (≃ 1/330 in)	94·2

on acid soil. The extreme pH limits in cultivated soils range between 4·5 and 8·5, an optimum for most crops being in the neighbourhood of 6·5. With the exception of a few, such as potato, rye and oats, all crops may fail below pH 5·3. Lime deficiency will result in low yields from crops sensitive to it, such as sugar beet, barley, swedes, turnips, sprouts, cabbage beans and similar market-garden crops.

A rough and ready test, popular for years, of ascertaining whether or not a soil was deficient in lime, was to test it with hydrochloric acid. Effervescence indicated no need for lime, while a negative result assumed lime deficiency. Absence of effervescence is not necessarily reliable evidence, however. A soil need not contain calcium in the form of carbonate to be in a suitable condition for plant growth; it is the total exchangeable calcium that matters, and a low concentration is normally shown by a high acidity (low pH). The lime requirement of the soil is the 'equivalent' oxide or carbonate which will bring the exchangeable calcium to the level necessary for healthy plant growth.

The problem of sampling the soil for tests is important, because the sample must naturally be representative of the area as a whole. Factors such as the nature of the herbage, crop condition and drainage must be noted and taken into consideration. Expert advice on the matter can be obtained from the National Advisory Service of the Ministry of Agriculture, and a number of agricultural institutions are only too willing to assist the farmer in a survey of the lime requirements of his soil.

There are numerous forms of lime available to the prospective user— B.H.P. (Best Hand Picked) lump lime, the grade of burning of which is immaterial; unscreened lime; 'small lime' or 'lime ashes'; certain types of waste lime; hydrated lime; or ground limestone or chalk. Any type of lime is suitable, from non-hydraulic to magnesian. There has been, and still is, considerable controversy regarding the suitability of the latter, but modern opinion is, on the whole, in favour of its acceptability.

A point which the user must take into account, however, is the neutralizing value of the lime or limestone he is going to buy. It is obvious that the cost, and the dosage, depend on the concentration of neutralizing body present. The figure will naturally be lower in ground limestone, for example, than in lump quicklime, in the theoretical ratio of 56 to 100. In the user's interests, the Fertilizer and Feeding Stuffs Act, 1926, requires that materials supplied under the Act shall carry a guarantee of their value, given by the producer in terms of the concentration of their active ingredient. In the case of lime products, their neutralizing value must be declared when tested by the method laid down in the Fertilizer and Feeding Stuffs Regulations, 1955.

Working on the figures given by the producer under the Act, a calculation of dosage is simple. A normal dressing can be taken as 1 ton of quicklime per acre. The rough equivalent of ground limestone will be 36 cwt; and so on, in terms of neutralizing value.

Quicklime may be applied in either spring or autumn, ground limestone and hydrated lime in any season of the year should necessity demand and opportunity arise. There is, however, one caution—never apply quick or hydrated lime at the same time as manure or ammoniacal fertilizers. The reason will be obvious to a chemist!

Limestone is also used as a source of calcium in cattle cake and of shell-forming material in *poultry grit*. Lime enters into the manufacture of *calcium cyanamide* and *sulphate of ammonia*, and of many proprietary insecticides and fungicides. Last, but not least, as *whitewash* it helps to brighten and disinfect farm buildings and outhouses.

Building and construction

The early use of limestone and lime in building by the Romans and Egyptians has already been mentioned in the Introduction. In the fifteenth century, a great revival of plasterwork followed the excavations of the baths of Titus, when work of such quality was revealed that enthusiasm spread from Italy to the whole of Europe. Stucco became popular, especially in London, but it is for mortar and internal plastering that a steady demand has existed to the present day.

Both limestone and lime are still used in building and construction. The harder forms of stone, which have crushing strengths of up to 25,000 lbf/in^2 are employed on an increasing scale for roads and for concrete aggregate, while ground limestone is one of the standard fillers for asphalt. Specially quarried and shaped limestone can still be seen in building.

Together with sand, slaked lime or hydrated lime forms the basis for *mortar* and *plaster*. Hydraulic lime sets by virtue of the hydration of its silicate/aluminate content, the semi-hydraulic class possessing this property to a lower and varying degree. The high-calcium and white chalk (non-hydraulic) limes set, with sand, through desiccation of the colloidal hydroxide, followed by slow carbonation.

With the advent of Portland cement, limes temporarily lost their popularity in mortar mixes. World practice has shown, however, that strength in mortar is not everything, workability, bond and watertightness being equally important, and the types of mortar recommended in British Standard Code of Practice C.P. 111—'Structural Recommendations for Load-bearing Walls' and B.S. Code of Practice C.P. 121.101—'Brickwork' include mixes of cement with non- or semi-hydraulic lime and sand. Eminently hydraulic lime and cement should not be mixed—if this type of lime is used, sand only should be added.

For both mortar and plaster, the lime should be slaked by the method appropriate to its type (see Chapter III). If non-hydraulic, semi-hydraulic or magnesian it should be 'run', with sieving to a milk, and for the first two types, allowed to stand for at least a fortnight; if magnesian, for 3 months. During this period, any hard-burnt material has an opportunity to slake and the calcium hydroxide micelles to adsorb water, to give the maximum *volume yield* of putty. If hydrated lime is used it is simply necessary to mix with water and leave for a minimum of 16 hours to let it fatten up.

The putty is then mixed with sand in the proportion required and is known as 'coarse stuff', for mortar and for plaster backing coats. If the mix has to stand for long before use, it must be protected from drying out. Then, immediately before use, it is, if required, gauged with Portland cement for mortar and external work, or with either cement or gypsum plaster for internal plastering. For plaster face coats, the putty, punched through a finer sieve, is either mixed with a lower proportion of sand than for backings, or used 'neat' with gypsum plaster gauging. It is, of course, impossible to give proportions of recommended mixes and methods of application in this book—for details, the reader is referred to the above Codes of Practice, also to British Standard Code C.P.211.201—'Internal Lime Plastering'.

Two interesting characteristics of lime putties associated with micelle formation are *plasticity* (or *workability*) and *volume yield*. A plaster is applied by trowel to a porous background and worked, by the plasterer, to a plane surface. If the plaster has a low power of water retention, it loses its workability before the plasterer can finish the surface properly, 'curling' under the trowel and 'ribbing'. The properties of high plasticity and high water retention against suction are possessed by lime putty to an outstanding degree when compared with other plasters.

Closely linked with plasticity is the *volume yield* of plastering putty obtainable from unit weight of original plastering medium, which confers the advantage of high spreading power, where lime is again superior.

The phenomena of workability and volume yield support the theory of hydrated colloidal micelle formation in suspensions of calcium hydroxide. It is of interest to note that the higher the CaO content of the original lime and the lighter its degree of burning, the better is its workability and the greater its spreading power.

British Standard 890–1940—'Building Limes' has been framed in an attempt to set a series of standards to which a lime must conform before it is acceptable for building purposes. The Specification embraces tests for quicklime and hydrated limes for plastering finishing coats, for coarse stuff and for building mortar. Methods of sampling are given, and conditions for tests which include composition, residue on slaking, volume yield, and workability. Specially framed for hydrated limes, in addition, are tests for fineness, soundness, and general expansion. The last two deal with the detection of unhydrated hard-burnt quicklime and 'water-burnt' lime particles in the product. These particles, being only slowly reactive, can slake in the applied plasterwork, perhaps weeks or even months later, and, by expanding, cause unsightly 'blows', 'pops' or 'blisters', as they are known in the trade. In putties from quicklime, the relatively long period of maturing before use provides a reasonable opportunity for their decomposition, and thus elimination; in the case of a reputable hydrated lime the amount is minimized by the rigid technical control of hydration and finally eliminated by air classification. If a hydrated lime is guaranteed by the manufacturer to meet the requirements of B.S. 890 for soundness, it can, as stated earlier, be used immediately after mixing to putty without fear of 'blowing', although it is wise to let it mature at least overnight to gain workability and volume yield.

Although the British Standard Workability Test (in B.S. 890) is effective in assessing the *relative* workabilities of lime putties at Standard Plastering Consistence, a really satisfactory method of measuring absolute plasticity or workability has not yet been devised. To complicate matters still further, extra stirring or working of the putty before test gives higher volume yield and workability at standard plastering consistence, through increased hydration of the calcium hydroxide micelles. Reproducible test conditions are therefore extremely difficult to attain. A detailed study of the rheological properties of lime putties is a field of research which can still yield much fundamental information.

Another very important building material, into the manufacture of which limestone enters, is *Portland cement*. Sand, clay and limestone or chalk are mixed in accurately controlled proportions, ground and slurried with water. The slurry is dried and clinkered in rotary kilns, and finally ground with the addition of a little gypsum to control the rate of setting. Portland cement, like building limes, must conform to the requirements of a British Standard.

Soil stabilization for roads

One of the most recently developed uses for lime, which has gained great favour in the U.S.A., is that of soil stabilization for roads. The action of lime in soil has already been discussed under 'Agriculture and Horticulture', and the reader will recall the power of flocculating colloidal clay particles and allied properties. The standard method of making a road is to replace the soil underneath to a predetermined depth, with hard (stone) aggregate, on which a special traffic surface is finally laid. It has been found that by admixture with relatively small amounts of hydrated lime (determined by laboratory tests) the original soil in the base can be stabilized, saving the cost of much of the depth of aggregate which was formerly required.

The geological formations in the British Isles, the readier availability of aggregate, and our more conservative attitude, have limited this use of lime here so far.

Tanning

Lime is used in the tanning industry for dehairing and plumping the hides or skins. Its role in dehairing hides is to assist sodium sulphide, which it does by opening up the fibre structure and removing interfibrillary protein. The hairs are loosened in their sheaths and thus more easily removed.

The hides are immersed in a milk of lime from either slaked quicklime or hydrated lime. Loss of actual hide substance by hydrolysis is avoided by the addition of 0·01%–0·05% of either ammonia or dimethylamine, or by using a 'mellow' lime liquor, in which hides have previously been treated and which contains degradation products of protein hydrolysis.

The hides next begin to plump. This must not be confused with swelling. Plumping, which is caused by the hydration of the collagen in the fibres, persists through the subsequent tanning process, and results in a full-bodied leather, whereas a swollen hide collapses. The water held in loose combination by the calcium hydroxide micelles is available for the hydration of the collagen, the process being initiated by osmosis. In simple terms, the calcium hydroxide acts as a water carrier, performing a function not effective with water alone, or with other hydroxides.

After plumping, the limed hide, usually known as a pelt, is passed to subsequent stages of the tanning process.

It will be obvious to the reader that a slow-settling milk of lime will be the most efficient in use, and the higher its calcium oxide content the better. It must be free from unslaked or water-burnt lime, particles of which could burn the hide if they settled on it and slaked *in situ*. Again the advantages of using a milk from hydrated lime are patent.

From the point of view of chemical composition, the lime should be low in magnesium oxide, which coarsens the grain of the leather, and in iron oxide, which tends to stain it.

In the case of sheepskins, the flesh sides are painted with a wet mixture of whiting, hydrated lime and sodium sulphide. The skins are piled skin to skin and wool to wool for about a day, when the wool is plucked out. The pelts are then limed in the usual way.

39

The chemical composition of the lime is even more important in the treatment of skins for the more delicate and decorative end products such as fine leather goods.

Water treatment—the lime-soda process

Modern methods of water treatment are numerous, and the literature on the subject so extensive, that no attempt will be made here to survey the matter as a whole, but simply to indicate the role of lime.

The composition of water varies according to its source; in chalky country, for instance, waters are generally very hard, whereas moorland waters may be relatively soft, and coloured by organic matter.

The treatment applied depends on the use to which the water is to be put, but the general principle is the same—the removal or destruction of the undesirable ingredients.

The presence of soluble bicarbonates of calcium and magnesium confer temporary hardness on a water, i.e. the types which can be removed by boiling, when the insoluble carbonates are formed. Temporary hardness is removed in practice by the use of lime:

$$Ca(HCO_3)_2 + Ca(OH)_2 = 2CaCO_3\!\downarrow + 2H_2O$$

$$Mg(HCO_3)_2 + 2Ca(OH)_2 = Mg(OH)_2\!\downarrow + 2CaCO_3\!\downarrow + 2H_2O.$$

Calcium carbonate is soluble in water to the extent of only about 18 parts per million, and magnesium hydroxide to about 9 parts. The treatment therefore reduces the concentrations to sufficiently low values for most purposes.

Permanent hardness in a water is caused by the presence of chlorides, sulphates and nitrates of calcium and magnesium. The magnesium salts are converted by lime to magnesium hydroxide, e.g.

$$MgCl_2 + Ca(OH)_2 = Mg(OH)_2\!\downarrow + CaCl_2.$$

Although the magnesium has been removed it has been replaced by a calcium salt. The calcium salts as a whole can now be removed by the addition of soda ash:

$$CaCl_2 + Na_2CO_3 = CaCO_3\!\downarrow + 2NaCl.$$

40

e and sodium carbonate is the principle of the
:ss for softening water.

ively high concentrations of magnesium com-
.fy, because the magnesium hydroxide formed is
: cases, it is customary to add sodium aluminate
)c which occludes the magnesium hydroxide and
ι clear water much more quickly and efficiently.
.iicklime, slaked to a milk, or hydrated lime,
mally used for water softening. The type should
i-hydraulic of relatively high calcium oxide con-

Pap

The   *f* paper consists essentially of the production of
cellulose   :aw material such as wood or esparto grass with
caustic soda,   g the cellulose, and converting it to paper by a
mechanical process. Certain higher grades of paper are then coated with
Satin White or precipitated chalk to improve the surface. Lime is used in
four processes: causticizing (or production of caustic liquor), bleaching,
Satin White manufacture, and precipitated chalk manufacture.

In the production of *caustic liquor*, quicklime is treated with a solution
of sodium carbonate. Caustic soda is formed and calcium carbonate precipitated:

$$Ca(OH)_2 + Na_2CO_3 = 2NaOH + CaCO_3.$$
$$\downarrow$$

The calcium carbonate is either filtered off or allowed to settle and the
supernatant caustic liquor drawn off for digesting the cellulosic deriva-
tives. Since a coarse-particle precipitate is desirable which will filter readily
or settle to a compact cake, a solidly-burnt grade of lime is used (see Chapter III).

Bleach liquor is made by passing liquid chlorine into milk of lime. It is
essential to keep an excess of calcium hydroxide in suspension, or the
liquor becomes acidic and decomposes. The milk must therefore be reactive
and slow settling, and must be slaked and run from a lightly-burnt grade
of non-hydraulic quicklime or mixed from a non-hydraulic hydrated lime
and water. Hydrated lime is preferable because of its consistent composition, allowing the quick preparation of a milk of lime of known strength.

Satin White is a complex compound produced by adding aluminium

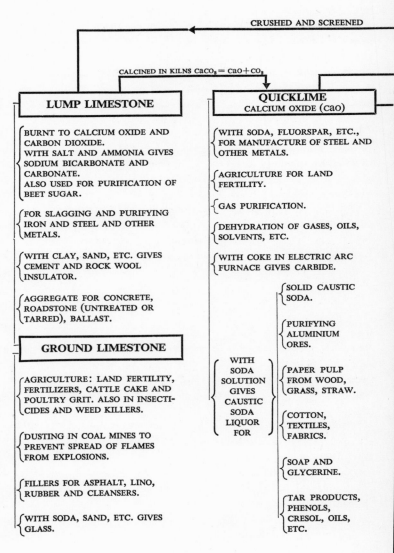

CRUSHED AND SCREENED

CALCINED IN KILNS $CaCO_3 = CaO + CO_2$

LUMP LIMESTONE

BURNT TO CALCIUM OXIDE AND
CARBON DIOXIDE.
WITH SALT AND AMMONIA GIVES
SODIUM BICARBONATE AND
CARBONATE.
ALSO USED FOR PURIFICATION OF
BEET SUGAR.

FOR SLAGGING AND PURIFYING
IRON AND STEEL AND OTHER
METALS.

WITH CLAY, SAND, ETC. GIVES
CEMENT AND ROCK WOOL
INSULATOR.

AGGREGATE FOR CONCRETE,
ROADSTONE (UNTREATED OR
TARRED), BALLAST.

GROUND LIMESTONE

AGRICULTURE: LAND FERTILITY,
FERTILIZERS, CATTLE CAKE AND
POULTRY GRIT. ALSO IN INSECTI-
CIDES AND WEED KILLERS.

DUSTING IN COAL MINES TO
PREVENT SPREAD OF FLAMES
FROM EXPLOSIONS.

FILLERS FOR ASPHALT, LINO,
RUBBER AND CLEANSERS.

WITH SODA, SAND, ETC. GIVES
GLASS.

QUICKLIME
CALCIUM OXIDE (CaO)

WITH SODA, FLUORSPAR, ETC.,
FOR MANUFACTURE OF STEEL AND
OTHER METALS.

AGRICULTURE FOR LAND
FERTILITY.

GAS PURIFICATION.

DEHYDRATION OF GASES, OILS,
SOLVENTS, ETC.

WITH COKE IN ELECTRIC ARC
FURNACE GIVES CARBIDE.

WITH
SODA
SOLUTION
GIVES
CAUSTIC
SODA
LIQUOR
FOR

SOLID CAUSTIC
SODA.

PURIFYING
ALUMINIUM
ORES.

PAPER PULP
FROM WOOD,
GRASS, STRAW.

COTTON,
TEXTILES,
FABRICS.

SOAP AND
GLYCERINE.

TAR PRODUCTS,
PHENOLS,
CRESOL, OILS,
ETC.

42

LIMESTONE ROCK
CALCIUM CARBONATE ($CaCO_3$)

HYDRATED UNDER CONTROLLED CONDITIONS TO A DRY POWDER
$CaO + H_2O \rightarrow Ca(OH)_2$

AKED USING
CCESS WATER

MILK OF LIME
CALCIUM HYDROXIDE SUSPENSION ($Ca(OH)_2$)

MIXED WITH
EXCESS WATER

HYDRATED LIME
CALCIUM HYDROXIDE ($Ca(OH)_2$)

BUILDING AND CON-
STRUCTION FOR MAKING
BRICKS, MORTARS AND
PLASTERS, WHITEWASH,
SOIL STABILIZATION.

ETHYLENE OXIDE, AN
INTERMEDIATE FOR
PLASTICS AND SURFACE
ACTIVE AGENTS,
DETERGENTS.

PURIFICATION OF ORES,
AND PREPARATION OF
NON-FERROUS SALTS.

WITH ALUMINIUM SUL-
PHATE GIVES SATIN
WHITE, A GLOSSY
COATING FOR PAPER.

SOFTENING AND
PURIFYING WATER
SUPPLIES.

PLUMPS AND DEHAIRS
SKINS AND HIDES FOR
LEATHER.

USED FOR SCOURING
WOOL TO REMOVE ACIDS,
ETC.

WITH FATS AND OILS
FOR CANDLES AND
GREASES.

WITH HIDES AND BONES
FOR GLUE AND
GELATINE.

PURIFICATION OF OILS
AND PETROLS.

PURIFYING COMMON
SALT.

RESINS, PLASTICS, RUBBER.

WITH CHLORINE GIVES
BLEACH LIQUOR FOR
COTTON AND PAPER
MAKING, CHLOROFORM.

TREATMENT AND
PURIFICATION OF
SEWAGE AND EFFLUENTS.

WITH CARBON DIOXIDE
GIVES PRECIPITATED
CHALK FOR TOOTH-
PASTE, COSMETICS, ETC.

WITH CHINA CLAY, ETC.,
IN MAKING POTTERY
AND CERAMICS.

PURIFYING INGREDIENTS
FOR PAINTS, VARNISHES
AND PIGMENTS.

WITH GASWORKS
LIQUOR GIVES AMMONIA
FOR SULPHATE OF
AMMONIA.

MEDICINALS, e.g.
PENICILLIN, ASPIRIN,
ETC.

MANUFACTURE AND
PURIFICATION OF DYE
SUBSTANCES.

ORGANIC AND
INORGANIC COM-
POUNDS AND SOLVENTS.

TREATING PRODUCTS
OF WOOD DISTILLATION.

WIRE DRAWING.

PURIFICATION OF CANE
SUGAR AND SYRUP.

WITH CHLORINE GAS
GIVES DRY BLEACH
POWDER (OR CHLORIDE
OF LIME).

AGRICULTURE AND
HORTICULTURE FOR
LAND FERTILITY AND
PEST KILLER. FOR
MAKING LIME-SULPHUR,
NICOTINE, AND OTHER
FUNGICIDES.

SOIL STABILIZATION IN
ROAD CONSTRUCTION.

FOR MAKING MEDICINAL
CALCIUM HYDROXIDE.

FILLER IN RUBBER AND
OTHER MATERIALS.

MANUFACTURE OF
GREASES AND FOR SODA
LIME FOR ABSORPTION
OF CARBON DIOXIDE.

43

sulphate to milk of lime. It forms as a glistening white gelatinous precipitate, which is separated by filter press and stored as a damp cake till used. It must not be allowed to dry out, since its colloidal properties cannot be restored by re-wetting. Used alone or generally with china clay, it gives the glossy white finish characteristic of certain high-class papers.

Obviously the lime, quick or hydrated, used for this purpose must be the purest obtainable, low in iron and free from black specks and traces of impurities which give coloured salts.

The method generally used in the trade for the preparation of *precipitated chalk* for coating paper is to pass carbon dioxide into milk of lime, which is run from specially selected pure quicklime (non-hydraulic) or from hydrated lime of the same type.

Soda ash

Anhydrous sodium carbonate (soda ash) is used to the extent of many millions of tons a year in the manufacture of glass, soap, textiles and chemicals. Although natural soda deposits in a number of places are worked to a limited extent, the production of sodium carbonate is mainly dependent on limestone and salt as raw materials.

The process employed is the Solvay or ammonia-soda process which appeared about 100 years ago and within a space of 40 years entirely replaced the older Leblanc process, which also used limestone and salt.

The overall effect of the ammonia-soda process is shown by the stoichiometric equation

$$2NaCl + CaCO_3 = Na_2CO_3 + CaCl_2$$

but there is no practical way of achieving the result by direct reaction between sodium chloride and calcium carbonate—indeed, the reverse reaction predominates. The desired result is reached by several steps of reaction. In the ammonia-soda process these are:

$$(a) \quad 2NaCl + 2NH_4HCO_3 = 2NH_4Cl + 2NaHCO_3 \downarrow$$
$$(b) \quad 2NaHCO_3 = Na_2CO_3 + CO_2 \uparrow + H_2O$$
$$(c) \quad CaCO_3 = CaO + CO_2 \uparrow$$
$$(d) \quad CaO + H_2O = Ca(OH)_2$$
$$(e) \quad 2NH_4Cl + Ca(OH)_2 = 2NH_3 \uparrow + CaCl_2 + 2H_2O$$
$$(f) \quad 2NH_3 + 2CO_2 + 2H_2O = 2NH_4HCO_3.$$

The sum of these equations gives the overall stoichiometric relation, but it is the step shown by equation (a) which characterizes the ammonia-soda process. It is accomplished by carbonating an ammoniacal brine in columns known as Solvay towers. Crude sodium bicarbonate is precipitated and is separated and calcined (equation (b)) to give anhydrous sodium carbonate and gases which are returned to the process for use in carbonation.

The conversion of sodium chloride in the Solvay tower is incomplete, so that the solution separated from bicarbonate contains ammonium and sodium chlorides, together with dissolved ammonia and carbon dioxide, which are recovered by heating. Solid ammonium chloride can be manufactured from this solution, but the demand for it is trivial compared with that for sodium carbonate. Its ammonia content is too valuable to allow it to be wasted, and efficient operation of the process depends on recovering the ammonia for re-use, which is done by distilling the solution with milk of lime (equation (e)). This yields the ammonia, which is absorbed in brine, a solution containing calcium chloride equivalent to the sodium carbonate made, and unreacted sodium chloride. Solid calcium chloride can be obtained by evaporation of this solution, with separation of sodium chloride, but again the demand is very small compared with that for sodium carbonate, and in most ammonia-soda plants all the effluent from the distillation is run to waste.

The lime for ammonia recovery and the carbon dioxide content of the product are obtained simultaneously by burning limestone with coke in shaft kilns (equation (c)). This must be done where the carbon dioxide is needed, so that lime kilns are a necessary and very prominent feature of an ammonia-soda plant. The use of limestone in this way serves a double purpose—it provides a gas rich in carbon dioxide and at the same time a means of recovering the ammonia. The limestone used must be of very good quality. If all the raw materials were absolutely pure, the only waste would be the unreacted sodium chloride and 1·05 tons of dissolved calcium chloride for each ton of sodium carbonate. The limestone and fuel, however, contain impurities which appear in the lime as magnesia, alumina, iron oxide and silica in various states of combination, including combination with calcium oxide as silicates and aluminates, which do not decompose in the distillation stage and appear in suspension in the effluent. Sulphate as an impurity in the brine is converted to a precipitate of calcium sulphate by the milk of lime, and any carbon dioxide left in solution before distillation gives calcium carbonate. Even with high-quality limestone the solids in suspension in the effluent of an ammonia-soda plant may be as much as 0·1 ton for each ton of product. These solids are commonly settled in large 'waste lime' beds before the clear liquor is discharged and because of the large scale of the operations present a serious problem. The value of pure raw materials, and especially of pure limestone, which can be made to yield a very reactive milk of lime, will be apparent.

The Manufacture of caustic soda by the lime soda caustic process

Until the advent of the electrolysis of brine in the manufacture of chlorine and caustic soda, the main process for caustic soda was based on its derivation from sodium carbonate by the causticizing reaction described under 'The Paper Trade'. Solid-burnt lime is added to a hot solution of sodium carbonate prepared from soda ash, or, when the manufacture is carried out at an ammonia-soda plant, from a suspension of crude sodium bicarbonate which has been decarbonated by the passage of steam. The following reaction occurs.

$$Na_2CO_3 + CaO + H_2O = 2NaOH + CaCO_3 \downarrow .$$

It is incomplete, an equilibrium is set up, from which a solution containing about 10% of caustic soda can be obtained. The solid-burnt lime gives a precipitate of carbonate which settles to a compact mass from which the supernatant caustic liquor can be siphoned. The carbonate sludge is washed with water and the settling and siphoning repeated till the bulk of the caustic soda is recovered.

Alternatively, the calcium carbonate may be separated in a centrifugal filter, where the coarse precipitate from solid-burnt lime gives a compact, easily washed filter cake.

The liquor is evaporated in stages, during which the sodium salt impurities separate and are removed. Completion of the evaporation gives caustic soda in the molten form which can be cast into drums.

In recent years the demand for chlorine has been increasing more rapidly than that for caustic soda. Since caustic soda is produced at the same time as chlorine in the electrolytic process, electrolytic caustic is gradually displacing lime-soda caustic and may ultimately render it obsolete.

Sugar purification

The crude juices from cane or beet contain acids, gums, resins, fibre and adventitious impurities. The raw liquor is filtered, heated, and milk of lime added, which neutralizes the acids to form insoluble calcium salts, and coagulates and precipitates the colloidal gums and resins. Excess lime dissolves to produce an alkaline solution. Calcium saccharate is, of course, formed as well.

Carbon dioxide is then passed into the liquor under controlled pH conditions, decomposing the saccharate and reacting with the lime to give a precipitate of calcium carbonate which acts as further coagulant and absorbent for the impurities. On filtration, a clear yellow syrup is obtained, which is passed through activated charcoal, evaporated and cooled to yield purified sugar crystals.

Some sugar refineries buy quicklime and use flue gas as the source of carbon dioxide, others take limestone and burn it themselves to provide both reagents. The stone or lime should be of high purity, since a foodstuff is involved.

Wire drawing

Wire is drawn or stretched from rods of steel, copper or other metals. In the case of steel the rods or coils are treated with acid, washed and dipped in milk of lime, which is allowed to dry as a thin coat. The rods are then drawn through hardened steel dies till of the required diameter. Before passing through each die, the wire runs through a bath of lubricating agent, such as soap powder. The lime itself acts as a lubricant and refractory coating, preventing carbon from the burnt soap from pitting the wire.

The milk must be run from quicklime or hydrated lime of high CaO content and especially free from gritty particles.

Pharmaceuticals: cosmetics

Lime enters directly or indirectly into the manufacture of numerous drugs, pharmaceutical preparations and cosmetics. To cite only a few examples, it is used in the manufacture of calcium phosphates, which are now widely used as additives to flour, salt and other foodstuffs as extra sources of both phosphorus and calcium. Calcium lactate, calcium mandelate and other organic calcium salts used for medicinal purposes are made from lime. It enters into the manufacture of aspirin and penicillin, and into the extraction of theobromine, which is readily converted to the analgesic drug, caffeine. Precipitated chalk made from lime and carbon dioxide is widely used in pharmacy as an extender and filler in powders, pastes, ointments and medicines.

It is obvious that lime for drugs and medicinal uses must be the purest of the high-calcium or non-hydraulic type. It is sold to stipulated limits of arsenic, lead and similar toxic trace elements, concentrations of parts per million being in question. The British Pharmacopoeia lays down a limit of 4 parts per million of arsenic in calcium hydroxide itself, and even more stringent limits are required in lime to be used in the manufacture of some drugs and chemicals for foodstuffs.

Magnesium

Magnesium is normally manufactured by electrolytic methods from a source high in magnesia. Lime is used in the concentration of the magnesium salts in the solution by first precipitating iron and sulphate and then magnesium hydroxide, which is further treated for electrolysis.

High calcium or magnesian limes are suitable for the purpose.

Iron and steel

Both limestone and lime are used in vast tonnages for the manufacture of iron and steel; in fact, steel manufacturers can claim to be one of the largest consumers of high-grade lime in the country.

Iron is made by treatment of a mixture of iron ore, coke and limestone in a blast furnace. The mixed raw materials are fed through a hopper at the top of the furnace and are smelted with the aid of a blast of air blown into the lower part of the furnace through water-jacketed nozzles known as tuyères. The following overall reactions take place.

$$Fe_2O_3 + 3C \rightarrow 2Fe + 3CO \uparrow$$
$$2Fe_2O_3 + 3C \rightarrow 4Fe + 3CO_2 \uparrow.$$

As it passes down the furnace, the spongy metallic iron absorbs carbon. The limestone dissociates in the lower part, and the quicklime formed combines to form a slag with the silica, alumina, sulphur and other impurities present in both the ore and the coke. The iron sinks through the molten slag and is itself melted in the well of the furnace, the air blast burning out the bulk of the absorbed carbon.

The molten iron is then drawn into moulds, which have been sprayed with milk of lime, which prevents the molten iron from sticking to the moulds, thus facilitating easy removal.

Steel is manufactured from pig iron by reducing the carbon content still further and removing silicon, phosphorus and sulphur. This may be done in a Bessemer converter or in an open hearth furnace. In both processes quicklime is added to the melt to form a slag with the impurities.

It is also used for essentially the same purpose in the manufacture of special steel alloys.

Since one of the main functions of lime in steel manufacture is the removal of certain impurities, it follows that it must itself contain them in minimal amounts. In the case of sulphur, for instance, the highest quality steel lime must contain concentrations no higher than 0·07 % to 0·15%. When it is realized that the lime will also pick up sulphur from the fuel employed to make it, the reader will appreciate that one more problem in the production of really high-quality lime for industrial purposes is the provision of fuel of very low sulphur content.

Non-ferrous metals

The refining of copper, tin, zinc, mercury, lead, nickel and other metals requires lime at some point in the process, either for fluxing, precipitating, gas absorption, or for adjusting the pH of suspensions and solutions, also in froth flotation methods of separation.

Calcium carbide

Calcium carbide (CaC_2) is a primary heavy chemical extensively employed as a source of acetylene (for organic syntheses) and in the manufacture of cyanamide ($CaCN_2$), an important fertilizer. In a monograph on acetylene (in preparation at the time of writing), Dr D. W. F. Hardie describes the plant and processes for the manufacture of calcium carbide. All that need be said here is that it is made by heating graded quicklime and coke together in a furnace (usually electrical) at high temperature. The reactions which take place are still the subject of controversy, but the starting and end points may be conventionally represented by the equation

$$CaO + 3C \rightarrow CaC_2 + CO \uparrow .$$
$$\text{(quicklime) (coke)} \quad \text{(calcium carbide)}$$

The molten carbide is tapped off into iron bogies, allowed to cool and finally crushed or ground for subsequent use.

Bleaching powder

The preparation of bleach liquor on site has been described in the uses of lime in the paper industry. Industrial bleaching powder is manufactured from dry hydrated lime and chlorine gas. The reaction is much more complex than the average textbook leads one to believe, as is the composition of bleaching powder. For both industrial and tropical bleach, i.e.

bleach that is stable under tropical conditions, the process must be rigidly controlled so that the available chlorine content of the finished product is high and the moisture low. The hydrated lime must be very pure, since certain impurities prevent high available chlorine values being obtained, or even act as catalysts in the decomposition of the bleach.

Dyestuffs

Lime or hydrated lime enters into the manufacture of dyestuffs or their intermediates in a large variety of ways. As a low-cost base, it is used for neutralizing acid intermediates: for saponification and hydrolysis, either *per se* or after causticizing. As a source of calcium, it is employed to form either soluble or insoluble salts, and, finally, as a dehydrating agent for solvents and intermediates.

Glass

There are many kinds of glass nowadays, but the common variety used for the manufacture of bottles, sheet glass, etc., is made from a mixture of limestone, sodium carbonate and sand. The dried ingredients are fired to give a viscous melt of sodium calcium silicates, which is then 'formed' as required.

For the colourless glasses, the iron oxide (Fe_2O_3) content of the limestone must be as low as 0.03%–0.04%.

Colliery stone dusting

A very important safety use of ground limestone is the dusting of coal-mine roadways to prevent the propagation of explosion flames. When the coal face is blasted by explosives, the blast wave, travelling along the galleries, raises coal dust in a cloud. Coal dust and air form a potentially explosive mixture, but the limestone dust (often waterproofed if the mine is damp) spread over the floors and sides of the roadway or on loose shelves over coal conveyors is also dispersed by the blast wave and forms a barrier to any explosion flames.

The limestone used must be low in silica, in order to minimize the risk of the respiratory disease known as silicosis.

Sewage and effluents

In sewage treatment lime neutralizes acids, coagulates colloidal matter, and acts as a deodorant, disinfectant and fungicide. It aids the filtration or settlement of sewage sludge. Similarly, in trade effluent treatment it is used for neutralization, coagulation and precipitation.

Coal gas and by-products: petroleum

When coal is heated coal gas and coke are formed, with liquor by-products. The gas can be purified by the use of quicklime or limestone and oxides of iron, and the aqueous liquor, which contains ammonia, distilled with milk of lime. The ammonia given off is absorbed in sulphuric acid to produce agricultural sulphate of ammonia.

The heavier by-product liquor contains phenols, cresols and sulphonnated oils. It is treated with caustic soda made *in situ* from sodium carbonate and solid-burnt lime. The phenols and cresols dissolve as sodium salts, and are separated from the sulphonated oils, which are used to make surface active agents.

Carbon dioxide gas is then passed into the solution of sodium salts. The phenols and cresols are freed as oils, the sodium ion combining with the carbonate ion to form sodium carbonate, which is re-treated with solid-burnt lime to give fresh caustic liquor.

Crude petroleum is digested with milk of lime to remove sulphur compounds. Sulphuric acid dissolves certain impurities and the sulphuric and organic acids are neutralized by lime and the insoluble calcium salts separated. Finally, dry, very reactive quicklime is used to remove water and clarify the oils.

Organic chemicals

Quicklime or hydrated lime is used as an absorbent, catalyst, neutralizing and/or hydrolyzing agent in the preparation and purification of many *organic acids* such as acetic, benzoic, citric, lactic, oleic, palmitic and tartaric acids; in the purification of *albumin*, and the preparation of *acetone*. It is a purifying agent in the manufacture of *solvents* such as benzene, carbon tetrachloride, chloroethylene, trichloroethylene, naphthols and pyridine. Hydrated lime, converted to bleach liquor, reacts with acetone to give *chloroform*. Milk of lime is used as a neutralizing and hydrolysing agent in the manufacture of *propylene oxide*, a starting point in many organic syntheses.

Lime also enters into the separation and purification of the tobacco extracts to give *nicotine*, preparations of which are used in insecticidal sprays.

Sand lime bricks

As compared with the normal fired building brick, sand lime bricks are made by an autoclaving process. Lightly-burnt quicklime, suitably crushed, is either slaked to a dry powder separately, matured, carefully sieved free from stone and unslaked lime and then mixed with sand, or is allowed to mature as such with damp sand till fully slaked. Alternatively, proprietary hydrated lime is used in its place, eliminating the sieving and maturing.

Further sand is then added in the required proportion, and sufficient water to enable the mix to be pressed into bricks. After a short drying period, the bricks are autoclaved, when reaction between the calcium hydroxide and the sand results in the formation of silicates sufficient to give a unit of adequate strength for many building purposes. There is a British Standard Specification for Sand Lime Bricks to which all reputable makes conform.

The hydrated lime, whether proprietary or made *in situ*, must above all else be sound before use, i.e. free from unslaked or water-burnt lime, which, under the rigorous conditions of autoclaving, will result in 'pops' or 'blows' on the surface of the brick, or even in weakness or disruption of the brick.

Other uses

Quicklime or hydrated lime is also used in the following industries. *Cotton* to make caustic soda or bleach liquor: *wool* for scouring: *textiles and fabrics* to make caustic; as a neutralizing agent, absorbent and scouring agent; *ceramics* as a base and source of calcium: *rubber* as absorbent, accelerator, carrier, catalyst, coagulator, dehydrator: *paint* as a precipitant, saponifier and solvent: *varnish* as neutralizer, precipitant and saponifier: *pigments* for neutralizing and precipitating: *soap* for caustic, saponifier, and, directly, in calcium soaps: *candles* as a saponifying agent: *greases* as saponifier and dehydrator: *glue* as a hydrolyser and solvent: *gelatine* to neutralize and hydrolyse: *resin* as a solvent, precipitant and neutralizing agent: *plastics* in intermediates: *wood distillation* as neutralizing agent and absorbent: *glycerine* as neutralizing agent: *salt* to remove calcium and magnesium salts in the purification: *sodium borate, peroxide, phosphate, thiosulphate* as a base in purification: *calcium salts* as a source of calcium and as a base and precipitant in the manufacture of calcium arsenate, silicide, phosphates, etc.: *ferrocyanides* in neutralization, precipitation and purification: *soda-lime* as one of the ingredients: *potash* as extraction agent from potash ores: *manganese dioxide* as precipitant: *lead sulphate and carbonate* in the purification, for neutralizing, etc.: *penicillin* as a neutralizer and source of calcium: *precious metals* to provide protective alkalinity in the cyanide process.

Limestone, in the ground form, is used as a filler in *lino, rubber* and some *cleansers*: in *ceramics*, as a source of calcium.

BIBLIOGRAPHY

Introduction, historical and classification
Chambers's Encyclopaedia (George Newnes Ltd.)—Section on *The Lime and Limestone Industries* (contributed by F. P. Stowell).

Geological
NORTH, F. J.—*Limestones, their origins, distributions and uses* (1930).
OAKLEY, K. P., MUIR-WOOD, H. M.—*The Succession of Life through Geological Time*, British Museum (Natural History) (1956).
FEARNSIDES, W. G., BULMAN, O. M.—*Geology in the Service of Man* (1961).
TWENNOFEL, W. H.—*Principles of Sedimentation* (1950).
Ministry of Housing and Local Government—*Planning Maps and Explanatory Texts, No. 4 Limestone* (1957).

The solubility of calcium carbonate
FREAR and JOHNSTON—*J. Amer. chem. Soc.*, *51*, 2082 (1929).

The system $CaCO_3$—CaO: lime burning
JOHNSTONE—*J. Amer. chem. Soc.*, *32*, 938 (1910).
AZBE—*Rock Products*, *12*, 50 (1927).
FURNAS—*Rock Products*, *13*, 32 (1931).
ZAWADSKI—*C.R. Acad. Sci., Paris*, *194*, 1160 (1932).
NODA—*J. Soc. chem. Ind. (Japan)*, *36*, 137 (1933).
MATSUI and ORS—*J. Soc. chem. Ind. (Japan)*, *36*, 155 (1933).
BOREL—*Chim. et Industr.*, *271* (1934).
HACKSPILL—*C.R. Acad. Sci., Paris*, *203*, 1261 (1936).
NODA and KAN—*J. Soc. chem. Ind. (Japan)*, *42*, 229 (1939).
HELAN—*Stavivo*, *21*, 163 (1940).
HELAN—*Stavivo*, *22*, 98 (1941).
CLARKE and CLIFFORD—Unpublished information.
STOWELL, ANDERSON and FORSEY—Unpublished information.
Chambers's Encyclopaedia—Section *Lime and Limestone Industries*.
KNIBBS and GEE—*Lime and Limestone*.

The system CaO—$Ca(OH)_2$: slaking, hydration
AZBE—*Rock Products*, *12*, 50 (1927).
POZIN—*Zavodskaya Lab.*, 1041 (1934).
KUZNETSOV—*J. Chem. Ind. (USSR)*, *14*, 1333 (1937).
BAUER—*Pit and Quarry*, *7*, 39, 140 (1947).
CLARKE and CLIFFORD—Unpublished information.
STOWELL, ANDERSON—Unpublished information.
Chambers's Encyclopaedia—Section *Lime and Limestone Industries*.
Imperial Chemical Industries' Technical Service and Informatory Literature.

The association of Ca(OH)₂ with water

KOSMAN—*Z. Elektrochem*, *25*, 159 (1919) and *26*, 173 (1920).
KOHLSCHÜTTER and ORS—*Z. Elektrochem*, *25*, 159 (1919).
KOSMAN—*Chim. et Industrie*, *5*, 317 (1921).
JUSTIN, MUELLER—*Rev. gen. Colloides*, *3*, 73 (1925).
RAY and MATHERS—*Industr. Engng Chem.*, *20*, *4*, 415 (1928).
BASSETT—*J. chem. Soc.*, 1770 (1934).
DAWIHL—*Tonind. Zeitung*, *58*, 581 (1934 *et seq*).
STALEY and GREENFIELD—*Proc. Amer. Soc. Test. Mat.*, 953 (1947).
STOWELL—Unpublished information.
ANDERSON—Unpublished information.

Uses

Imperial Chemical Industries Technical Service and Informatory Literature.
STOWELL—*Chem. and Ind.*, *62*, 382 (1943).
British Standard B.S. 890—1940—*Building Limes*.
British Standard Codes of Practice C.P. 111 and C.P. 121.101 (*Mortar and Brickwork*).
British Standard Code of Practice C.P. 211.201 (*Lime Plastering*).
The Fertilizer and Feeding Stuffs Act, 1926.
The Fertilizer and Feeding Stuffs Regulations, 1955.
BESSEY, G. E.—*Sand Lime Bricks*, National Building Studies Special Report No. 3, London, H.M.S.O.

Statistics

Central Statistical Office, Annual Abstract of Statistics No. 96, (1959) and No. 97 (1960).
Agricultural Lime Department (U.K.). *Consumption of Agricultural Lime in the United Kingdom.*
Ministry of Agriculture, Fisheries and Food—*Planning Maps, Explanatory Texts, No. 4 Limestone* (Issued by Ministry of Housing and Local Government, 1957).

GLOSSARY OF TERMS

Birefringent.   Exhibiting double refraction.

Captive tonnages.   The tonnages of limestone (or chalk) produced for private consumption by some manufacturers (notably of cement, steel and sugar), and drawn from their own quarries. The figures are therefore not directly available for overall statistical analysis.

Consistence.   Before the workability and volume yield of a lime putty can be determined under the conditions laid down in British Standard 890—*Building Limes*, the consistency of the putty must be adjusted to a specified standard value. This value is known as Standard Plastering Consistence, and is achieved by addition or removal of water.

Gauging.   The recognized term in the building trade for the addition of an agent to a mix to modify its properties, notably its set. If cement or a gypsum plaster (normal or retarded calcium sulphate hemihydrate, for example) is added to a lime/sand mix to accelerate its set, the latter is known as 'a gauged lime/sand mix' or, more specifically, as 'a lime/sand mix gauged with cement (or gypsum plaster)'. Conversely, if lime is added to a cement/sand mix to retard its rate of set, or improve its workability and other properties, the mixture is called 'a cement/sand mix gauged with lime'.

Gotten.   A term used in the quarrying industry from time immemorial. Getting (or winning) is the act of obtaining limestone in the form of discrete, handleable lumps or fragments from the massive, continuous deposit, and the resulting material is known as 'stone gotten'.

Lime burning.   Again, a very old term, still in active use, for the conversion of limestone to lime, by the action of heat, on a manufacturing scale. *Vide* 'light-burnt lime' and 'solid-burnt lime'.

Running.   A trade term used to cover the overall process of converting quicklime to a milk or putty. It comprises slaking, sieving and maturing.

Soundness.   A hydrated lime is 'sound' when it contains no particles of unslaked lime, water-burnt lime, or any other similar type liable to decompose in subsequent processes, causing either expansion or localized high temperature.

55

PRINTED IN GREAT BRITAIN BY

W. & J. MACKAY & CO LTD, CHATHAM